Mississippi: The Closed Society